The Bishop's Wolf

A Young Pilgrim's Story-Guide to
The Saints & Heroes of Hereford Cathedral

RICHARD WILLMOTT

Illustrated by
SANDY ELLIOTT

for Eleanor and Thomas

LOGASTON PRESS

How to follow the children's route through the Cathedral

This story is set in and around Hereford Cathedral. The route that Lisa, Sonia, Josh and Matt take is shown by the numbers on the map opposite. Wherever there is a number in the story, there is one on the map to show where they have got to.

It is probably best to read the story without looking at the notes, but if afterwards you want to find out more about anything that has a dagger (†) by it, you will find some explanations at the end of the story.

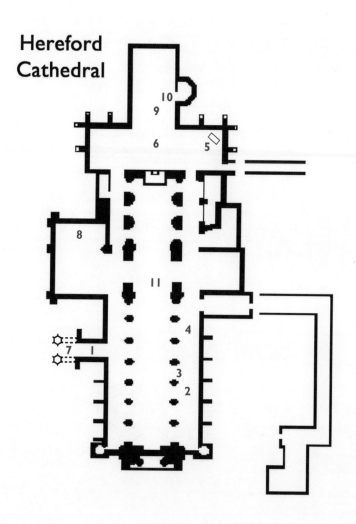

Hereford
Cathedral

10

9

6

5

8

11

4

7 1

3

2

First published in 2019 by Logaston Press
The Holme, Church Road, Eardisley, HR3 6NJ, UK
www.logastonpress.co.uk
An imprint of Fircone Books Ltd.

ISBN 978-1-910839-39-3

Designed and typeset by Richard Wheeler

Printed and bound in the UK

Logaston Press is committed to a sustainable future for our business, our
readers and our planet. This book is made from paper certified by the Forest
Stewardship Council.

British Library Catalogue in Publishing Data.
A CIP catalogue record for this book is available from the British Library.

The Bishop's Wolf

'Yesss!' said Matt. 'Another day of freedom!'
But his mother looked less impressed as
she turned off the local news.

'How stupid to close the schools again –
there's hardly any snow left and I can't afford a
second day off work. You'll have to go round to
someone whose mum's at home today.'

At that moment her mobile started to buzz.
'Hello? Oh hi. No I can't – I'll never catch up
if I don't go in today. Oh, do you think she
would? Brilliant – I'll drop him off in ten
minutes. Bye.'

'Right – get your coat. We're off.'

'But where are we going, Mum?'

'Josh's mum says that Mary Ellery will look
after you both today.'

'What, Lisa's mum? I'm not going.'

'Oh yes you are. Get your coat on.'

'But Lisa's the one …' Matt gave up: his mother wasn't listening.

If Matt was gloomy, Lisa and her friend Sonia, who had already come round, were equally unimpressed. 'You *couldn't* have said those boys could come round. Oh Mum, you've ruined what was going to be a fabulous day.' And sure enough, it only took ten minutes for a squabble about whether to watch a box set or Sky Sports to turn nasty.

'Right, you lot, you're not sitting all day in front of the telly. You can do some shopping and get some fresh air at the same time.'

'But Mrs Ellery,' said Sonia …

'She means it,' urgently whispered Josh, who had not forgotten an uncomfortable telling-off after retrieving his football from what had previously been a fine clump of daffodils in the Ellerys' front garden.

'Yes, I do,' said Mary Ellery, giving him a look that suggested that she hadn't forgotten either, 'but I'll give you some money to buy a hot drink while you're out. Now find your coats and get going.'

After buying some groceries in Hereford and going into High Town to get hot chocolates, they wandered fairly aimlessly down Church Street towards the Cathedral. There was no one much around except for another group of two girls and two boys who drifted after them into Church Street. Matt's mother had been right: the snow had nearly all melted and when they got to the Cathedral Close all that was left was a muddy sludge round some holes that workmen had dug and then abandoned.

Disappointed that there wasn't enough for a snowball fight, Josh instead squeezed some of the slush into a sort of ball and, sneaking up on Lisa, tried to stuff it down her neck. She swung round, kicking him sharply on the shin, and Josh yelped. The other three laughed and angrily Josh turned on Sonia, who was nearest, and began to push her towards one of the workmen's holes, while the group who had followed them started laughing and jeering.

'Stop it – it's not worth it,' said Matt.

'Well, she shouldn't …'

Josh broke off as a sudden, deep growl grew

more menacing. Standing with its rear legs in the hole and its front paws on the edge of the hole was an enormous grey dog with all its teeth showing and its eyes focused on Josh. They froze for a moment and then, just as they were about to sidle away, the dog dropped back into the hole and they could see that it had been digging.

'What on earth's it doing?' asked Josh.

'It's *under* the earth, not *on* it,' said Lisa.

'Very clever,' said Josh sneeringly – he could feel the bruise coming up on his leg and had no intention of being amused.

'Look,' called Matt. 'Has it found a bone? No. Hang on – it looks like a box.'

And sure enough, the great grey dog had unearthed a narrow, red box. What happened next was distinctly odd. He picked the box up in his teeth, scrabbled his way out of the hole and put it at their feet.

'Don't touch it,' said Sonia. 'He'll bite you.' But in fact, it was when the children stepped back from the box that the dog growled and when they came forward again that he stopped. It was not the sort of dog that would

wag its tail, but they sensed its approval as they looked down at the box, and when Josh asked if they should take it (for some reason it didn't seem daft talking to a dog) it seemed pleased.

'Let's look at it in the porch,' suggested Sonia when they had brushed the worst of the mud off. So there in the North Porch of the cathedral (**1**) they opened the box and found something they never forgot.

In the box was a short roll of old calfskin. †
'This feels odd,' said Matt, who had taken

5

it out. 'It feels smooth, more like plastic than paper, and it's got something written on it. It looks like poetry. Here, see if you can read it.'

Lisa took the roll and, in a puzzled voice, read out:

> *The only measure of real treasure*
> *Is whether it stay without decay*
> *When life and gold do fade away.*
> *To find the treasure*
> *That brings true pleasure,*
> *Go in to the Garter –*
> *Then look for the martyr.*

'That's just gibberish', said Lisa. 'How can you go *into* a garter? You'd probably strangle yourself.'

'Hang on,' said Matt, looking over her shoulder. 'It doesn't say go *into* the garter, but go *in* – to the garter. Perhaps we ought to go in – into the cathedral – and see if we can go to a Garter. I know it sounds daft, but it's spelt with a capital G, so perhaps it means something different.'

'Well,' said Lisa, rather doubtfully, 'Mum said she didn't want us back before one, and it's freezing out here. Yeh, I suppose we might as well go in.'

They didn't notice the other group follow them in.

Inside it wasn't as dark as they had expected and they looked around wondering which way to go. Josh and Matt were attracted towards a great blue window on the opposite side of the nave. There were little flashes of red mixed in with the blue and the whole thing looked like blue flames flying upwards. Beneath was a monument saying 'Special Air Service' and candles were burning. (2) 'Wow,' said Matt, 'what a way to remember real heroes.'

Then Josh caught sight of the statue of a knight in armour lying on a tomb shaped like a great chest and turned round to have a look. (3) Matt followed and read a sign: 'Hey, how about this? This guy was called Sir Richard Pembridge and he fought at the battles of Crécy and Poitiers. I guess he's another hero.' He called to the girls, 'Here, come and look at this.'

Sonia and Lisa had stopped to chat, but now they moved slowly towards the tomb. Then Sonia looked up and saw it. 'Good grief!'

she said sarcastically, imitating the favourite expression of a teacher who always made Matt feel uncomfortable. 'I didn't think boys ever noticed anything, but you've found it.'

'Found what?' they asked together.

'The garter, of course,' she said, pointing at the knight's leg. Then she began to laugh. 'Don't tell me. You didn't see it, did you? Of course you didn't.'

The boys grinned rather foolishly, but admitted they hadn't. 'Well at least we led you to it,' pointed out Josh.

'And what's more,' added Matt, seeing a chance to show the girls that he wasn't stupid, 'I can tell you what the Garter is and why it's spelt with a capital letter.

'I did a project on it last term. It all began when a lady dropped her garter and the king, Edward the Third, picked it up for her and tied it back on. Some of the people watching sniggered and that's when Edward said the words that became the motto of his new order of the Knights of the Garter: *Shame on the person who thinks shameful things.*'

'No, that was the story told by the French to discredit our noble order,' said a man's voice. 'They wanted people to think that our sovereign lord was just a ladies' man and not a serious fighter and rightful King of France. No, the garter was just one of the straps we used to fix our armour and so we tied the King's motto to it. What we meant was shame on the King's enemies who pretended to believe that his claim to the throne of France

9

was wrong and shameful. And we did bring shame to them on the battlefield. *Honi soit qui mal y pense*,' he added grimly. †

All four of them had turned to face the speaker, lying there on the tomb, still as a statue, except that his lips were moving and his eyes were focused on them. When he stopped, they just stood there, stunned. In the end it was Matt who had to ask a question: 'Do you mean … were you really … what I mean is … sir … er … did you help to win those battles at Crécy and Poitiers? That's cool. You must have been really brave.'

'It wasn't "cool" in your sense of the word, nor in mine. You sweat a lot in battle even if you're not wearing armour, and there's nothing "cool" in your sense about killing other people: ask the men in the SAS. Nor in the end did it take much courage. We were surrounded and heavily outnumbered at both Crécy and Poitiers. There was nowhere to run away to. When it's *kill or be killed*, it's quite easy to decide which.'

'But I'm sure you *were* brave.'

'Bravery's not about weapons, although

it may mean facing other people's weapons. If you want to understand it, you must find the martyr. To look death in the face without flinching or losing your faith: that is true courage.' Silence followed and the statue lay unmoving.

They stared at each other, doubtful. 'Have I just been hallucinating?' asked Matt.

'I think we all have,' said Sonia. Then she realised that she was still holding the calf-skin from the box. 'Hang on. Didn't he mention the martyr? That's what it says here, *look for the martyr*. But where?' They looked back at the statue, but the stone monument gave no hint of life. Then suddenly it seemed to them that the dog at Sir Richard's feet stirred in the way dogs do when another one is about. Instinctively they looked up to see the cause. Right in the distance they just saw the great grey dog disappearing round a corner.

As they walked east along the South Aisle (4) looking for the dog, Lisa glanced up and paused for a moment, looking at one of the more brightly coloured windows. 'You're keen on history,' she said to Matt. 'Who's that up there?'

Matt looked up at the window, which
showed a man in a cloak with a star on the
shoulder surrounding a red cross. The man
had very long hair and was being greeted in
the street by a man on his knees. 'It's another
Knight of the Garter,' said Matt, 'and, wait a
minute … yes, his red cross is surrounded by
a star and not a garter. That means he must
be the king. With hair that long I reckon he's
Charles the First or Second.'

'Oh come on. Stop showing off. At this rate we'll never find this martyr,' said Josh.

Behind him Matt heard murmurs: 'Yeh, boring! What a boff, what a loser!' Annoyed, he glanced over his shoulder to see the shadowy group who were following them laughing, but he followed Lisa, Sonia and Josh towards where they had seen the dog disappear. As they reached the end of the aisle they could see no sign of the dog and looked around for a martyr's tomb. However, all they saw at first was a dark wooden object in the corner. (5)

'Not much sign of a martyr here. I wonder if there's anything behind that old bit of wood. We might find the treasure there,' said Lisa.

'There was treasure behind it once,' said a man with wild frizzy hair who was wearing strange red clothes.

'Oh, I suppose it's already been found and taken away?' asked Sonia.

'It wasn't that kind of treasure: it was bravery, not gold.'

'Was it the martyr, then?'

'No, but a man inspired by him. Years ago, that "old bit of wood", as you call it, was the pulpit where the priests stood when they were teaching the people. † When I was eight years old, I once hid behind a pillar watching a brave man telling off Parliament's Puritan soldiers. † They had captured the city and they came into the cathedral to stop the music and to smash any carvings in stone or pictures in glass that they disapproved of. Dean Croft was in charge of the cathedral in those days and he stood in that pulpit and told them off so fiercely that some of them were quite rattled. They didn't know how to answer and so instead they pushed their muskets against his chest and threatened to shoot him, but their commanding officer stopped them.' †

Matt poked an imaginary musket at Lisa, who snapped at him and told him to grow up.

'So what happened to him?' asked Josh hastily.

'Oh, the threats didn't prevent him from standing up for what he believed in, but he couldn't stop them throwing him out of the cathedral and out of his house. It was not until fifteen years later at the restoration of Charles the Second that he was able to come back.

Soon after that he was made bishop.'

'Is that the Charles who is shown in that window down there?' asked Matt, wanting to show he knew something about it.

'No that's his father, Charles the First, the one who had his head chopped off. His picture's there because he had visited Hereford a few months before, to thank the people of Hereford after they had successfully resisted an earlier siege. However, shortly afterwards Parliament's soldiers finally captured the city by a trick. Charles was executed, but Dean Croft lived a long life and had many friends. In fact, he's buried over there next to his closest friend.'

15

The four of them looked, and there were two grave slabs side by side, and carved across where they joined was a pair of hands holding each other.

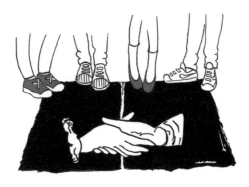

'Yuk! Just like girls,' said Josh.

'They didn't go round holding hands, if that's what you're thinking,' said the young man with a laugh. 'But they were true friends, and that's what the carving means.' He looked at them and added, 'Love isn't having soppy feelings; it's looking out for each other – even when you *are* feeling grumpy. One way to discover what the love of God means is to start caring for other people. Perhaps if you tried loving in that sort of practical way, you would understand the carving …' he paused, '… and not argue so much.'

The four of them looked a bit sheepish
at this and so, as if to spare them further
embarrassment, he went on, 'Anyway, if you're
looking for the martyr, all you need to do is
turn round.'

Immediately they caught sight of some
brightly coloured panels on a free-standing
pillar. (**6**) They quickly went to them, not
noticing the other group following them.

'Good grief! What's this thing?' asked Sonia.
'It looks like a medieval strip cartoon.'

She heard mocking laughter and a voice
behind her saying, 'Yeh, kids' stuff,' but didn't
see who it was and decided to ignore it.

'In fact,' she went on, 'I think that's just what
it is, and I think it tells the story of our martyr.
We've found him.'

There, sure enough, on the central pillar
were some vividly painted pictures telling the
story of St Ethelbert, a king of East Anglia in
the days when England was still divided into
lots of little kingdoms. He was not only good-
looking, it seemed, but good as well, and he
had left his kingdom to marry Aelfrida, † the
daughter of Offa, king of Mercia. However,

once Offa had discussed it with his wife, he had a *different* idea. He and his wife were afraid that Ethelbert might use the marriage as a way of taking over Mercia and so they gave orders that his head should be cut off, which it was, with his own sword.

'Typical men!' exclaimed Lisa. 'It's all violence. And anyway, where's this treasure. This is just a silly old story. Why have they got such stupid names?'

Again there were voices in the background: 'Yeh, stupid!'

'Aelfrida was no more stupid a name in my time than Lisa is in yours,' said a soft voice. 'And here is a treasure that *will* stay without decay. It wasn't just Ethelbert's love for *me* that made him special. It was his love for *everyone*. Even at the end, when he knew he was going to die, he never stopped caring and praying for other people and not himself. He followed the example of his master, Christ, who forgave the soldiers even as they were nailing him to the cross, and who was more bothered about arranging for his mother to be looked after than about his own painful death. Ethelbert's prayers to God for other people were so powerful that even after his death a blind man who picked up his head received his sight again.'

'That's just a story. What I want to know is where this treasure is,' grumbled Josh.

'Josh!' protested Sonia.

'Ethelbert knew where the treasure was. He told me, before they captured him, that on his way here he had a dream of a column of light more splendid than the sun, and a wonderful bird with gold tips to its wings soaring upwards into the beauty of heaven. It was the same light that came down to where his body lay when they threw it in the marsh. Many years later someone else understood that dream of light, and if you persevere, so will you.'

They looked around to see who had been talking to them, but could only see some tourists at the far end of the Lady Chapel † and the other group of two girls and two boys lurking in the shadows.

'Talk about weird,' said Lisa. 'Whoever it was knew my name, but where are they?'

'It sounded as if she was Aelfrida herself, but it couldn't have been,' said Sonia.

'Good grief, no,' said someone in the shadows, mimicking Sonia's favourite expression in a ridiculously posh voice.

'Who cares?' said Matt. 'I can think of some people who would look better without a head.' And he aimed an imaginary sword stroke at Sonia's neck just as she turned to see who was poking fun at her. He only just touched her, but she was furious.

'Sorry...' he started to say.

'You boys – first it was Josh and his stupid

snowball, and now you swinging your arms round like a maniac. Why don't you just stop and think for once in your life, you clumsy great bully, assuming you've got a brain at all.'

'That's boys for you. They're all the same,' said someone in the shadows.

'Steady on,' said Lisa. 'It was an accident.'

'Accident, accident, accident,' echoed round the building as the other group jeered and pointed.

'And why your mum had to let these two horrid boys ruin our day, I can't imagine.' Sonia stormed off, looking as if she might burst into tears. The others looked at each other uncomfortably and decided to follow her.

'We'd better go home,' said Lisa as they caught up with her. 'I daresay Mum will let us back in.' But as they left the cathedral and went into the North Porch (1) they saw that instead of snow there was cold rain blowing almost straight at them. As they paused, the grey dog appeared in front of them and growled.

'Okay brave boys, you can go first,' said Lisa sarcastically, but it was Sonia, who was determined to get away from the whole boiling

21

lot of them, who stepped forward first. The
dog's mouth was still not really open, but they
could see more of his teeth and the growl grew
stronger. Cross though she was, Sonia didn't
quite have the courage to go any further; it was
a very large dog and there was no sign of its
owner. She couldn't help a small sob. All the
same, in the end it was she who spoke first,
sniffing defiantly.

'I could cope with the dog,' she said, 'but
what's the point when I shall get soaked if I do.
I'm going back inside.'

'I guess we might as well all do the same,' said Lisa, wondering if she dared put an arm round her friend's shoulder. 'Hallo, what's that?' She was looking at a carving on the left-hand side of the arch into the covered part of the Porch. (7)

'It's a pilgrim,' said a woman, stopping for a moment before going into the cathedral. 'He's got a staff, and that little bag called a "scrip" is to put his food in and any money he might have. He may have been going to Jerusalem or Rome, but probably he was coming here to our own shrine of St Thomas Cantilupe. If you want to see it, just go inside, turn left and keep walking and you can't miss it.'

They followed the woman in and then, while she went off somewhere else, turned left. They didn't notice that they were being followed by a familiar grey shape, but the other group, who had apparently also developed an interest in the shrine, fell back a bit. In a few moments they came to the North Transept and saw it. (8)

'Goodness, I need sunglasses to look at that! How on earth did we walk past just now without noticing it?' wondered Matt. 'I suppose we were all too cross with each other.'

'Yup, I guess so,' replied Josh.

Sonia said nothing, but felt rather calmer as something large and warm brushed against her legs.

'So what *is* a shrine and, more importantly, *where's* this treasure?' wondered Lisa. 'Is it the bird with golden wings?'

'Some people would say that the treasure was right here.' The woman had come back, but now she was wearing a long blue gown-thing that went right down to her feet and a badge that said *Cathedral Chaplain*. 'Thomas Cantilupe, whose shrine this was, wasn't a martyr like St Ethelbert, but he was a learned man who became Chancellor of Oxford University and a trusted adviser of both Henry the Third and Edward the First. Most importantly of all, he was a hard-working bishop who cared for all the clergy and people round here, and especially the poorest and least important. Look, there's a picture of him up there. You can see he's a bishop because he's wearing one of those strange pointy hats that bishops wear. They're called mitres and the sticking-up bits are meant to remind us of the tongues of flame that were the sign that God's Spirit was coming down on the first disciples.' †

'I can't see him,' complained Lisa.

'He's up there kneeling on the left with his wolf just behind him in the bottom corner.'

'His wolf?' Matt was the one who spoke, but they all looked equally puzzled.

'It's a pun on his name,' she explained. '*Lupus* is the Latin for wolf as well as being the second half of Cantilupe, his name.'

'Nothing to do with melons, then?' said Josh with a smirk. The others looked at him pityingly.

'Take no notice of him,' said Lisa. 'Can you tell us what finally happened to him and why they made this thing for him?'

'Well, when he died he was in Italy on his way to see the Pope. Because he had wanted to be buried back at Hereford, they boiled the flesh off his bones …'

'That's gross! Oh, I can't believe it,' groaned Lisa.

'Cool,' said Matt.

'No it's not, Matt. It's revolting,' said Sonia making a face.

'Anyway, what happened next?' asked Josh.

'They buried the flesh there and brought the bones back here. After that, when sick people came here to pray close to the bones, they found that they were often cured. The authorities spent a very long time collecting all the evidence, but in the end the Pope's special committee in Rome agreed that he was a saint. After that they made Thomas Cantilupe's tomb into a special shrine, and although Henry the Eighth's men pulled down the new shrine that they built for him later in the Lady Chapel, this original one survived, and now it's been restored.'

'Are the bones still here?' asked Matt.

'I don't want to know,' said Josh, suddenly looking rather doubtful.

'There's only a tiny fragment here that was rescued and that was brought back when the shrine was restored.'

'I'm not bothered by bones,' said Lisa. 'I want to be a doctor. It was just the thought of boiling the body that got me. But what's the point of keeping a bit of bone?'

'Well, another Hereford man put it like this: "The bodies of the saints were once the conduit-pipes of the Holy Spirit." A conduit is a pipe and I guess what Thomas Traherne meant when he said that, was that saints are like pipes bringing the water that you need for life: not the stuff that Welsh Water pumps to you through the mains, but the experience of

God that your soul needs if it's not to die of spiritual thirst. That's why they wanted to treat the bones with respect.'

They still looked puzzled and the chaplain said, 'They say a picture's worth a thousand words. Why don't you go to the Audley Chapel and look at the Thomas Traherne windows.' At that moment some other visitors came up to ask a question and she turned away. The four of them hesitated, but the dog – was it really a dog? – was walking the way that the chaplain had pointed and, without really making a decision, somehow they followed it.

When they got round the corner the dog seemed to have disappeared and all they could see was the story of Ethelbert again.

'It must be up here,' said Josh, leading the way up some steps.

'You're always so sure you're right, aren't you?' said Lisa, irritated by his confidence when he had no more idea than the rest of them.

'Yeh, typical boy,' said Sonia.

'All right, we'll follow you, if you're so very, very smart,' said Matt sarcastically.

Suddenly each of them felt anger bubbling up inside them again as they remembered how annoying the others had been: Lisa realised her collar was still wet from that stupid snowball; Josh's leg still hurt from the kick; Sonia thought about being hit by Matt; and Matt remembered how he had been laughed at for being too clever. The other group had caught them up again and started to jostle and make pretend growling noises.

Suddenly there was a real growl and everybody turned to where the great wolf was standing at the top of the steps. (9) As they did so a sudden gleam of sunlight suggested that the weather was changing, and the tall narrow windows beyond flashed beautiful colours at them.

Mindful of the wolf – it had to be a wolf – they didn't quarrel after all, but went up the steps to see if there was some message in the windows. However, the sun quickly went in again and they couldn't work out any message. Then they saw the man with the wild hair and peculiar red clothes again, bending down to admire the wolf by a door into a small chapel.

Beyond them was a gleam of intense colour. (**10**)

'That must be it,' said Sonia.

Inside were four more windows, glowing with deep reds and greens and full of detailed pictures. In one of the middle windows was a young man dressed in red, standing in the middle of the countryside and bathed in a great stream of light coming down from the sun above.

'*You are as prone to love as the sun to shine,*' said Thomas Traherne, the man in red who was both in the window and standing beside them.

They didn't know what to say to this, and so

instead they looked at the picture to its right. It showed children playing in a street watched by kindly older people, with the tower of Hereford Cathedral rising above them.

'*The city seemed to stand in Eden,*' said Thomas.

'What are you on about?' asked Sonia.

'I saw God's love in everything that He made, both in the city and in the country.'

'Yeh, right – sure thing,' said mocking voices just outside the chapel.

Still unsure what to say, Lisa drew attention to the window on the far left. 'Look, you can see the cathedral again up at the top, but it's much further away and there's that man again … I mean is that you,' she turned to Thomas, 'running through the corn field?'

'That was the view near where I lived at Credenhill,' he replied. '*The corn was orient and immortal wheat.*' †

'Er, yeh … I suppose so,' said Lisa, who felt she had to say something in reply.

'Sure,' said a sneering voice, and there was laughter outside the chapel cut short by a low growl.

The four swung round, but the others had stepped back out of sight. Then they looked again at the windows.

'Even the tiniest of God's creatures are beautiful,' continued Thomas, pointing to a bright green beetle in the first window that they had looked at.

'Yuk, a beetle!' squeaked one of the voices outside.

'Stamp on it,' called another one.

'Crrrrunch!' laughed a third.

'Poor little beetle, boo hoo hoo,' said the fourth.

Suddenly Lisa, Sonia, Matt and Josh spun round and spoke together, 'SHUT UP!!'

Having turned, they looked properly for the first time at these others who had been following them and who, instead of retreating, were now peering quite boldly through the chapel screen. What they saw startled them, for they felt as though they were looking in a mirror.

'Yes, those *are* your voices,' said Thomas, a little sadly. 'But perhaps if you look at this remaining window they will be quiet.'

They turned to the last window and saw a tree, not of dark wood, but looking as if it was transparent, with light shining through it. You could see it was a tree alright, though, because of the grain of the bark. At its foot on the ground were ordinary birds pecking at the soil, but up above was an exotic bird soaring out of the light into heaven.

'*That cross is a tree set on fire with invisible flame, that illuminateth all the world. The flame is love,*' said Thomas.

'Illuminateth?' said Josh.

'The flame of love *lights up* the whole world. Can't you see the figure on the tree?'

Then they saw him: the figure of Christ on the cross which was not just a cross, but a tree of life linking heaven and earth. And as they looked at the cross that was a living tree, the sun came out again, and the tree became a great column of light. They couldn't have explained what the window meant, but they each felt a sudden surge of joy as if they were being lifted right out of themselves.

There was a long pause and then, rather shakily, they smiled at each other.

'I'm sorry,' said Josh.

'So am I,' said the others.

'We've none of us been fantastic today,' added Lisa. 'Let's forget what idiots we've been.'

'Agreed,' said Sonia; Matt and Josh just nodded.

They turned to leave the chapel with the light still shining behind them and saw that the others were still there, but something strange was happening: their shadowy forms were growing fainter and the sunlight was shining right through them until, finally, they disappeared.

'So, was that the treasure?' asked Sonia, but the man in red had gone. 'It's all very well, but all these people we've seen, or think we've seen – they're dead really, aren't they? What does it all mean?'

No one seemed to have an answer and so they started to wander away. Sounds in the distance had made them aware for a little while that quite a large group had come into the cathedral. Now the organ started to play and they realised that the choir must have come in to practise. They looked back from under the tower (11) to watch as well as listen, but at that moment the conductor stopped the choir.

'*What* is it you're singing about?' he asked, and he put on a bored voice. 'Greater love hath no man than to go out and buy a pizza for his mates?' Some of the boys in the choir laughed. 'No, I *don't* think so. Greater love hath no man than this: that a man *lay down his life for his friends* ... that he's prepared to *die* for them. Now come on; this is about God loving us so much that He's prepared to die on the cross for us.' He opened his arms in a sweeping gesture. 'It's what this whole place and everything we do is about. *Now*, sound as if you *mean* it! Let's go from the beginning again and remember:

"Love is as *strong* as death." Yes, ***strong.***'

The music started again and as the choir sang, Lisa looked up at a shiny zig-zag thing hanging down from the top of the tower on very thin wires that you could hardly see.

'That's beautiful,' she said. 'What is it?'

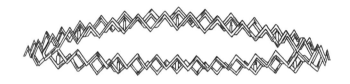

'Many things,' said Thomas Traherne, who had reappeared, 'but two above all. It's a reminder of the crown of thorns that the bullying soldiers shoved down on Jesus's head before they killed him on the cross, but amazingly, because he was prepared to die for us, it's also a crown of glory. What makes the thorns glorious is that He responded to our cruelty – to the crown of thorns – with the love and forgiveness on the cross that brought us new life. It's the same crown, but Jesus turns it into something glorious. And yes: Love *is* as strong as death.'

At that moment most of the choir went silent and they heard just one boy's voice singing a haunting solo: '*Who his own self bare our sins in his own body on the tree.*'

'You see?' said Thomas. 'The tree is the cross, the same tree you saw in my window that is alight with the flame of love.'

And now they heard one of the men singing a solo in his turn: '*That we, being dead to sins, should live unto righteousness.*' And on the word '*live*' his voice suddenly soared up.

That was when the four of them felt again as they had in front of the window. They seemed to hear again Thomas's words: 'That cross is a tree set on fire with invisible flame. The flame is love.' And then they saw, or they thought they saw, the tall figure of a bishop coming towards them with the great wolf striding beside him. On his head was his bishop's mitre, except that it wasn't just an *imitation* of flames:

37

it seemed to be actually sparking and crackling with electricity and shooting out flames. (As Sonia said afterwards, 'He seemed more like a lightning conductor for the Spirit of God, than a water pipe or whatever that woman said saints were!') And there, in front of them, in a pool of light, they saw the young king kneeling in prayer, and up from the bright column of light that shone on him they saw the great bird of paradise soaring through the crown of thorns that was also a crown of glory.

Then King Ethelbert looked up and said, 'I am convinced that neither death, nor life, nor rulers …'

'nor things present, nor things to come …' continued Thomas Traherne;

'nor height, nor depth …' added St Thomas Cantilupe;

'nor anything else in all creation,' they said together, 'will be able to separate us from the love of God, which is in Christ Jesus our Lord.' †

As they turned to leave, the choir were still practising. The last words that they heard were: '*show forth the praises of him who hath called you out of darkness into his marvellous light.*' †

'I'm starving!' said Matt, as they left the cathedral. They grinned at each other and set off home.

Notes †

Vellum (p. 5) was used for writing on in the Middle Ages. It was made from calfskin which was scraped and prepared. It lasts much better than paper. The Cathedral's *Mappa Mundi* (Map of the World) is written and painted on vellum.

Honi soit qui mal y pense **(p. 10):** This is the motto of the Order of the Garter. It is written in Norman-French because that was the language spoken by the king and nobles at the time. It means 'Evil be to him who evil thinks' or, as Matt translates it, 'Shame on the person who thinks shameful things'.

A **pulpit (p. 14)** is a raised, enclosed platform from which a clergyman preaches to the people in church (teaches them about God).

Parliament's Puritan soldiers (p. 14): There was a civil war between Charles the First and Parliament. The parliamentary soldiers were Puritans who thought the services in the Church of England were too elaborate. After they had won the war they abolished the Church of England, but it was re-established when Charles the Second was restored to the throne. During the Civil War, Hereford was on the King's side, but it was finally captured in 1645, a few months after Charles the Second had visited it, when the guards at one of the gates were tricked by some enemy soldiers in disguise.

Dean Croft (p. 14): A dean is the clergyman in charge of running a cathedral. Herbert Croft became Bishop of Hereford after the Civil War. A bishop is in charge of a whole region of the church, which is called a diocese. (Hereford diocese covers the whole of Herefordshire and the southern half of Shropshire as well as small areas of Worcestershire, Powys and Monmouthshire.) The commanding officer who told the soldiers not to shoot was Colonel Birch. There's a sculpture outside on the west end of the cathedral over the door on the left showing what happened.

Aelfrida (p. 17): There are lots of ways of spelling this name (some people call her Alfthrytha), just as there are several versions of the story.

The **Lady Chapel (p. 20)** is the chapel up the steps at the east end of the cathedral. It is dedicated to our Lady, or the Virgin Mary, the mother of Jesus.

Tongues of flame (p. 25): After Jesus had left his followers, the Holy Spirit gave them the skill, understanding and courage to start teaching other people about Jesus. The story describes the moment during the Jewish feast of Pentecost when they were inspired as being like tongues of flame settling on their heads. You can read about it in the Bible in Chapter 2 of the Acts of the Apostles.

Orient (p. 31): This means 'bright'. In Latin 'oriens' means rising, which is why the modern meaning of 'orient' is the east, where the sun rises, but in Thomas Traherne's time it could also mean 'bright' like the rising sun. Thomas Traherne grew up in Hereford at the time of the Civil War. He later became a priest and wrote a lot about how the universe shows the love of God. The remarks he makes that have been put in italics are taken from a book called *Centuries* (because he put his ideas in paragraphs that are grouped in sets of one hundred – in 'centuries').

The words the three saints of Hereford say (p. 38) come from verses 38 and 39 of the eighth chapter of St Paul's Letter to the Romans.

The music that the choir is rehearsing (p. 38) is by an English composer called John Ireland (1879–1962), and these are the full words (taken from various parts of the Bible):

Many waters cannot quench love, neither can the floods drown it. Love is strong as death.

Greater love hath no man than this, that a man lay down his life for his friends.
Who his own self bare our sins in his own body on the tree, That we, being dead to sins, should live unto righteousness.

Ye are washed, ye are sanctified, ye are justified in the name of the Lord Jesus.

Ye are a chosen generation, a royal priesthood, a holy nation;
That ye should show forth the praises of him who hath called you out of darkness into his marvellous light.

I beseech you brethren [brothers], by the mercies of God, that you present your bodies, a living sacrifice, holy, acceptable unto to God, which is your reasonable service.